Preschool Skills

All About Me and My House

This book provides fun practice in readiness skills for early learners. An appealing theme engages the attention of children as they complete the carefully chosen activities. The activities, which have been designed to prepare children for school, provide practice in beginning math, visual skills, fine-motor skills, language, thinking skills, and more! Children will enjoy exploring concepts related to *All About Me and My House* as they complete a variety of fun activities!

Skills in this book include:
**Counting • Patterning • Sizes • Visual perception
Thinking skills • Sequencing • Classification
And more!**

Written by **Marcia S. Gresko** and **Vicky Shiotsu**

Cover illustration by **Georgene Griffin**

Illustrated by **Susanne DeMarco, Georgene Griffin, Joyce John, Patty McCloskey, Gerry Oliviera, Becky Radtke,** and **Barb Tourtilotte**

FS132905 All About Me and My House
All rights reserved—Printed in the U.S.A.
Copyright © 2000 Frank Schaffer Publications, Inc.
23740 Hawthorne Blvd.
Torrance, CA 90505

ISBN 0-7682-0383-X

Table of Contents
Skills & Concepts

Busy Days and Nights

Draw a line to what happens next. Color.

Funny Faces

Cut out and match to make four funny faces.

FS132905 All About Me and My House

Watch Me!

Cut out the cards.
Use them to play a memory game.

Teacher: Have students work in pairs and give one copy of this page to each pair. Talk with the students about what the children are doing in the pictures. Then let students cut out the cards and use them to play memory match.

My Feelings

Color and cut out.
Staple with page 7 to make a book.

My Feelings

My happy face,
Look and see

A birthday party
Just for me!

1

My sad face,
Look and see

My kite stuck high
In a tree.

2

My angry face,
Look and see

My dog playing where
He shouldn't be.

3

My Feelings

Color and cut out.
Staple with page 6 to make a book.

My proud face,
Look and see

A special picture
Made by me.

4

My loved face,
Look and see

My mommy hugging and
Loving me.

5

Lots of faces,
Look and see

They are all just
Part of me!

6

FS132905 All About Me and My House

Getting Along

Circle the pictures that show the better way to behave.

About Me

Listen to your teacher read the rhyme.
Join in and say the rhyme with your teacher.

I have two  eyes.

I have two  ears.

I have one  mouth,

One nose.

I have two hands.

I have two feet.

I have 10 wiggling 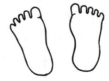 toes!

9

FS132905 All About Me and My House

Name

Bedtime

Help the sleepy child find her way to bed.

FS132905 All About Me and My House

Five Senses Riddle Book

Use this page with page 12. Cut, match, and paste the pictures from the bottom of this page.
Then cut and staple to make a book.

My Five Senses Riddle Book

You hear me go ding-a-ling. What am I?

1

Five Senses Riddle Book

Use this page with page 11. Cut, match, and paste the pictures from the bottom of page 11.
Then cut and staple to make a book.

You can taste me.
I am cold and sweet.
What am I? **2**

You can touch my soft warm fur. What am I? **3**

You can see me in the sky. I am white and fluffy. What am I? **4**

You can smell me as I bake. What am I? **5**

Can You Find These?

Find and color.

  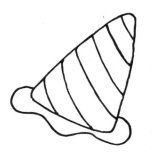 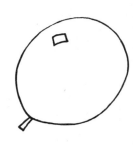

I Am Special

My name is _____.

I am _____ years old.

My eyes are _____.

My hair is _____.

Name _____

Where Are the Children?

Cut and paste each place next to the matching child.

In the Kitchen

Cut out the things that belong in the kitchen.
Paste them on the picture.

In the Living Room

Cut out the things that belong in the living room.
Paste them on the picture.

Skill: Fine motor coordination

Name _____

In the Yard

Help the children follow the path to their dog.

18

FS132905 All About Me and My House

In the Bedroom

Cut out the things that belong in the bedroom.
Paste them on the picture.

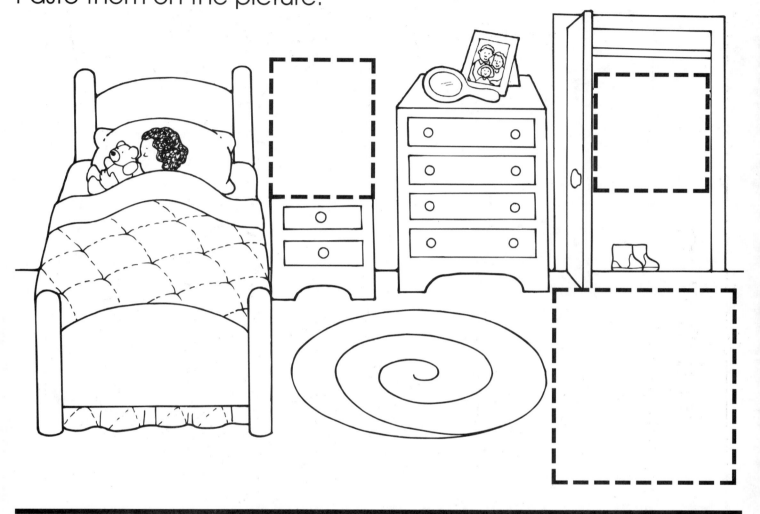

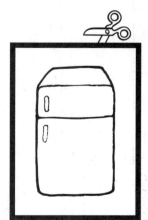

Look in the Closet

Count. Draw a line to the number.

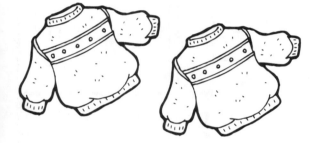

2

3

5

1

4

FS132905 All About Me and My House

Name_____

Look and Find

Find and color.

   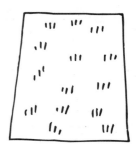

21

FS132905 All About Me and My House

Name _____

Fun in the Water

Connect the dots.

Trace the numbers.

FS132905 All About Me and My House

Fun at Home

Draw a line to what happens next. Color.

My Day

Say the picture words.
Listen to your teacher read the rhyme.
Join in and say the rhyme with your teacher.

dustpan

broom

fish

dish

bread

bed

What did you do in the morning?
What did you do in the morning?
I swept my room with a dustpan and  broom.
That's what I did in the morning.

What did you do at noon?
What did you do at noon?
I ate some fish from a yellow dish.
That's what I did at noon.

What did you do at night?
What did you do at night?
I had stew and bread, then went to bed.
That's what I did at night.

FS132905 All About Me and My House

Name _____

A Dollhouse

Cut out and paste.

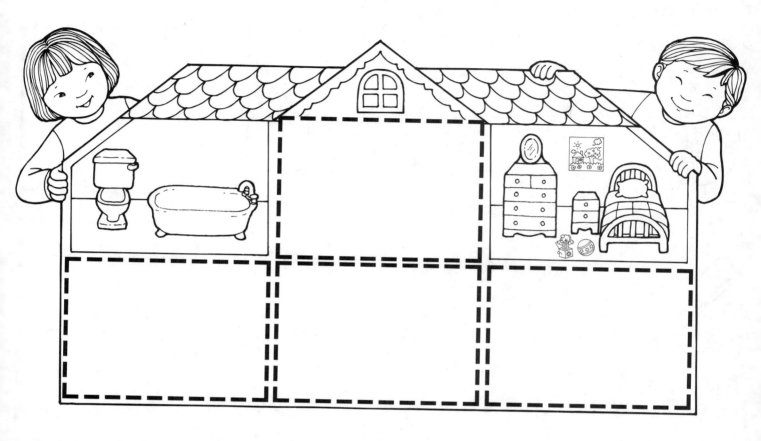

FS132905 All About Me and My House

Around the House

Find the pattern.
Paste the picture that comes next.

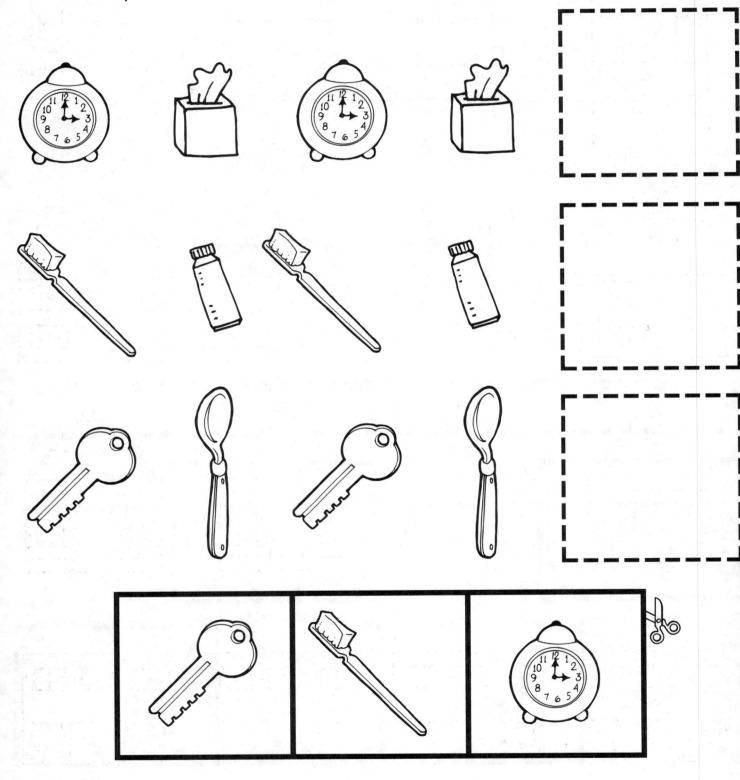

Skill: Visual discrimination

All Kinds of Homes

Color the three homes that are alike in each row.

FS132905 All About Me and My House

Name_____

Safety at Home

Color and cut out.
Staple with page 29 to make a book.

Safety at Home

1

Play safe! Stay safe!
Remember this each day.

Pick your toys up off the
    floor
When you're done for
    the day.

2

Play safe! Stay safe!
Remember this each day.

Don't climb on drawers,
    shelves, or chairs,
That's no way to play.

3

FS132905 All About Me and My House

Name _____

Safety at Home

Color and cut out.
Staple with page 28 to make a book.

Play safe! Stay safe!
Remember this each day.

Keep things like toys and
    tricycles
Off of your driveway.

4

Play safe! Stay safe!
Remember this each day.

Don't run out into the
    street,
A car might come your
    way.

5

Play safe! Stay safe!
Remember this each day.

Having fun, keeping safe,
That's the way to play.

6

FS132905 All About Me and My House

Name _____

Toys That Go

Color the biggest toy on each shelf **red**.
Color the smallest toy on each shelf **blue**.

30

Pretty Flower Pots

Color the flowers.

red

orange

blue

yellow

pink

purple

Where Do They Belong?

Draw a line from each to the matching group.

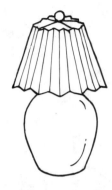